SUKI AND SAM

By Dr. Lisa Marotta

Illustrated by Dorothy Shaw

Love lives forever!
Lisa R Marotta PhD

Purple is for remembering!
Dorothy Shaw

DOODLE AND PECK PUBLISHING

Doodle and Peck Publishing
P.O. Box 852105
Yukon, OK 73085
(405) 354-7422
www.doodleandpeck.com

ISBN 978-1-7323637-1-7 (soft cover)
ISBN 978-1-7323637-4-8 (hard cover)

Library of Congress Control Number: 2018945701

~ DEDICATION ~

In memory of Mildred "Grammie" Williams and Suki.
Your unconditional love is with me always.

DR. LISA MAROTTA

~

To my Muse, Elizabeth.
Thank you for your inspiration and support.

DOROTHY SHAW

Samantha loved the yellow in her breakfast egg, the green of her backpack, and the bright orange stool at the kitchen table.

"You have an eye for color, Sam," said her art teacher.

Samantha also loved her dog, Suki. Suki's tongue was
glossy pink and the tufts of fur by her ears were inky
black. Samantha even loved Suki's biscuit breath.

Every morning, Samantha and Suki took walks by the mustard yellow tree, chartreuse green bushes, and salmon orange flowers blooming by the sidewalk. Suki's shiny gold tags jingle-jangle-jingled all the way home.

As Samantha grew taller, Suki grew older.

That meant gentle pats, doggy snores, and slower walks for a slower Suki.

One winter morning,
Samantha snapped her
fingers for Suki to come.

She didn't.

Suki was too quiet.

Her body lay still
and her fur was cold.

Suki wasn't breathing.

All the color drained from
Samantha's world.

"What's wrong?" her art teacher asked.
"Are you feeling okay?"

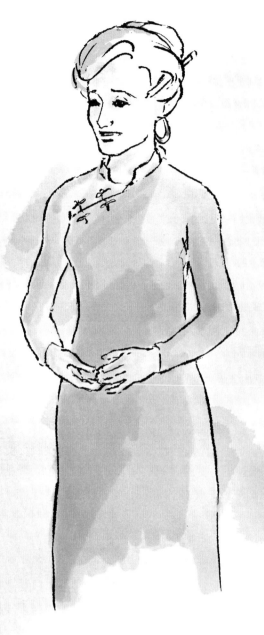

"I feel . . . nothing," Samantha whispered. "The colors died."

Samantha shuffled home and crawled back into bed.

No walks.

No painting.

Everything felt wrong without Suki.

Everyday her teacher would ask, "Do you feel like painting today, Sam?"

Samantha sniffled and stared at the blank canvas.

Until one day, when her teacher asked the same question, Samantha answered…

"**NO!**
I am too mad!

I hate that Suki isn't here to take walks."
Is there a color for mad? Samantha wondered.

She squeezed the
tube of red paint
and dipped her
brush on the
palette—
red tree,
red bushes, and
red flowers wilting
in the garden.

"Everything is
different now."

On the way home, Samantha glared at her neighbors walking their dogs.

"What do you feel like painting today?"
her teacher asked.

"I'm just **too sad** to paint since
Suki died," said Sam. "Hmmm…blue's probably
the color for sad," she wondered aloud.

Samantha squeezed the blue paint onto the
palette and lifted her brush.

As the blue paint filled the canvas, Samantha told
her teacher about all the fun times she shared with Suki.

Her teacher looked at the painting. "It's okay to grieve, Sam."

"It's okay to grieve."

"I wish she was here," Samantha said.

On the walk home, Samantha shared
a funny memory of Suki with her neighbors.
The dogs wagged their tails.

Maybe they remembered Suki, too.

At school Samantha again stared at a new blank canvas.

She glanced at the empty space at her feet.

She closed her eyes and pictured Suki.

The pink of her tongue, the gold of her tags,

and the inky tufts of fur sticking out from her ears.

Samantha understood Suki wasn't coming back.

One spring morning Samantha ate her yellow breakfast egg on the orange stool by the kitchen table.

She grabbed her green backpack and headed to school.

On the way, she noticed a
new color blooming in the garden.

Samantha waved at her neighbors, petted their dogs, and smiled,
remembering when Suki had pranced by her side.

In art class, Samantha squeezed
red onto her palette, and then
reached for the blue.

With a big brush, she mixed
the colors together.

She painted a yellow egg, her green
backpack, and the bright orange stool
at the kitchen table—all next to a
purple Suki, resting by her feet.

Samantha painted more—a mustard yellow tree,
chartreuse green bushes, and blooming salmon
orange flowers—each with a purple Suki.

"Purple?" asked her art teacher.

"Purple is for remembering,"
Samantha said with a smile.

Each day,
Samantha painted
Suki back into
her life.

One
canvas
at
a
time.

TO PARENTS AND EDUCATORS FROM DR. MAROTTA

It's not surprising that children form a special attachment with their pets. Pets are patient listeners, offer unconditional love, and are eager playmates. Every pet has a unique personality and often becomes part of the family. As an adult, you understand that all living things die, including our pets. Although grieving is a healthy and natural process, this loss may be your child's first experience with the reality of death. It may feel overwhelming. You can help your child with open communication, compassion, and acceptance of their feelings.

Artwork and grief-work are a healing combination. George Rodrigue's "Blue Dog" paintings were the inspiration for this book on love, loss, and healing. Something familiar about Blue Dog's soulful yellow eyes reconnected me with every precious pet that I had loved and lost. I wanted to create a story that would help grieving children use art to "draw out" their feelings.

I believe every child is an artist. With encouragement from a trusted adult, children can learn to share their experiences and process confusing feelings with art. These pictures then become a medium to begin healing through remembering. Be prepared to get re-acquainted with the family pet through your child's eyes. This can be a special bonding time for you both, and the pet pictures will become a treasured memorial. I hope you will be comforted by your child's resilience as they share their sorrow.

All living things die—but love lives forever.

ACTIVITY

The Color of Grief introduces the idea that feelings can be expressed through art. If possible, have pictures of the family pet nearby with paints, crayons, or colored pencils, and plain sheets of paper or small canvases. Over the next few weeks invite your child to draw pictures and encourage them to share a special memory. Help your child identify feelings as they come up during drawing. Healing develops with time as your child makes the connection that all feelings are okay and memories feel good.

Here are some additional ways to support your child through pet bereavement:

✔ **Prepare** a simple, truthful story about the death of the pet and tell your child as soon as possible. Keep in mind that your child will use your story later to explain the death to themselves and others.

● **Things to consider:** Was the death caused by accident, advanced age, or terminal illness? Was the dog euthanized? If so, be prepared to talk briefly about quality of life or an ending to suffering.

● **Avoid misinformation** or, misleading information, that can trigger other emotions. Explanations that refer to the pet as "falling asleep," or "sent to the farm," are confusing and scary, and they reduce your credibility.

✔ **Listen carefully** to your child's level of understanding and attend to their questions.

- **Typical questions:** Why did he/she die? Where is my pet now? (This may mean physically or spiritually) Will he/she be alive tomorrow?

- **Children sometimes assume that bad things are their fault.** Reassure your child that death is a natural ending to life and the child did nothing wrong.

✔ **Preschool and early elementary** aged children sometimes struggle with the concept of the permanence of death. They may expect the pet to be alive tomorrow or living underground. Kindly correct their misunderstanding and be prepared to repeat explanations often depending on the level of confusion.

✔ **Older elementary** aged children may understand that death is permanent, but can develop anxiety about the death of other family members including parents. Attend to your child's concern and be honest that death is the ending of life while reassuring that other family members are in good health if this is the case.

✔ **Be patient** if your child has temporary behavioral regressions at meals, play, and bedtime. These routines become sad reminders of the absence of their pet.

✔ **Ceremonies are soothing** rituals that can also serve as practice for human funerals. Encourage your child to help plan a simple service that could include playing music, sharing memories, and/or planting a tree.

✔ **Drawings and/or photographs** may be displayed at a memory table in your home. Your child might also want to add mementos like collars or toys to the special space.

✔ **Some children request a new pet** right away. It is understandable that they want their difficult feelings to end quickly. Postpone getting a new pet if possible to give your child the opportunity to fully resolve their pet loss and bond appropriately to a new pet. Reassure your child that you will consider adopting a new pet "when the time is right."

✔ **Some children delay grief expression or show extreme grief responses,** even in families with open communication and compassionate listening. Common grief complications include multiple prior deaths, traumatic pet death, and stress or mental illness in the family. If you are concerned about your child, please consult a professional for additional support.

Positive and loving experiences during bereavement will help your child now *and with future losses* which come in many forms—big (beloved family and friends) and small (moving to a new home and/or changing to a different school). I hope *Suki and Sam* help your child "draw out" their multicolored feelings of grief.

ACKNOWLEDGEMENTS

Once upon a time I believed that writing a book was a solitary process. Just me and my idea. Wow, was I wrong. There were so many people who helped me and my idea develop into a published book.

I am grateful to:

The Inklings Critique group: Brandi Barnett, Kelly Bristow, Martha Bryant, Dee Dee Chumley, Mari Farthing, Sonia Gensler, and Shel Harrington. Your patience and feedback sustained me through the countless revisions of this story.

My Beta Readers: Stephanie Clinton, Dr. Anne Jacobs, Julie Kohl, Ashley Thompson, and Katie Trattner. Your keen observations and input helped me fill in some missing pieces.

Oklahoma Writers Federation, Inc (OWFI) and The Society for Children's Book Writers and Illustrators (SCBWI). For awesome conferences and encouraging friendships.

Charles Gosset. Your coaching transformed the way I approach my writing and life in general.

Marla Jones. Thanks for taking a chance on me and connecting these words with Dorothy Shaw's artistic eye.

Mom. Who always knew I would write a children's book. You were right.

Dad. For teaching me how to set goals and persevere.

Lindsay Whitworth and Kate Marotta. Thank you for the sweet notes and thoughtful phone calls of encouragement while I worked on this book.

Sal Marotta, the best boyfriend ever. Your love and humor always lift me up and cheers me onward.

Sable, Bingo, Suki, and now Dude. Thank you for long walks, cuddle time, and biscuit breath kisses. You've left pawprints on my heart forever.

DR. LISA MAROTTA